When I Was Little

by Ann Takman

D0096348

HOUGHTON MIFFLIN
BOSTON

PHOTOGRAPHY CREDITS: Cover © Horst Herget/Masterfile; Toc © Rolf Bruderer/Masterfile; 2 © Victoria Blackie/Dorling Kindersley/Getty Images; 3 © Terry Vine/Blend Images/Getty Images; 4 © Rolf Bruderer/Masterfile; 5 © Corbis/Jupiter Images; 6 © Jose Luis Pelaez, Inc./CORBIS; 7 © Lori Adamski Peek/Riser/Getty Images; 8 © Horst Herget/Masterfile; 9-10 © Kevin Dodge/Masterfile

Printed in China

ISBN-13: 978-0-547-01667-2
ISBN-10: 0-547-01667-0

12 13 14 15 0940 17 16 15 14
4500496268

Look at the picture.
I am the baby.

Now I am big.
I can read
with my aunt.

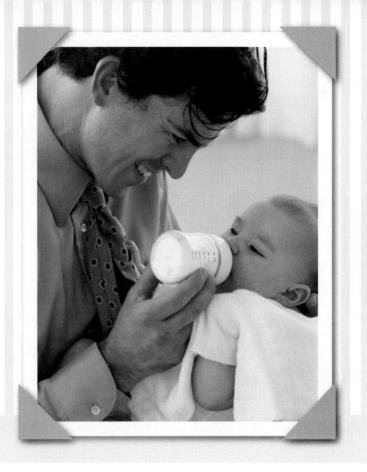

Look at the picture.
I am the baby.

Now I am big.
I can smile
with my father.

Look at the picture.
I am the baby.

Now I am big.
I can ride
with my mother.

Look at the picture.
I am the baby.

Now I am big.
I can walk
with my grandmother.

And I can swim
with her, too!

Responding

✔ **TARGET SKILL** **Main Idea** What is the main idea of this book? How can you tell?

Write About It

Text to Self Draw a picture of yourself when you were a baby. Draw another picture that shows what you look like today. Label your pictures.

WORDS TO KNOW

I

LEARN MORE WORDS

aunt | baby

✔ **TARGET SKILL** **Main Idea** Tell the main idea about a topic.

✔ **TARGET STRATEGY** **Summarize** Stop to tell important ideas as you read.

GENRE **Informational text** gives facts about a topic.